I AM
BECAUSE I
CHOOSE

by Patrice McLaurin ** Illustrated by Dian Wang

I Am Because I Choose by Patrice McLaurin

Books may be purchased in quantity and/or special sales by contacting the author at pmclaurin@patricemclaurin.com or the publisher at sales@khemrahpublishing.com.

Published by: KhemRah Publishing, LLC. Buford, GA
Illustrated by: Dian Wang
Creative Director: Darren McLaurin

ISBN: 978-0-9973152-7-1
Library of Congress Control Number: 2020909859
MARC Org Code: GaBukP

1. Children's 2. Picture 3. Poetry 4. Social Emotional Learning 5. Character Education

First Edition

khemrahpublishing.com

For My Squad,

Darren, Khemi and Rahsun.

Your support during my journey has been unwavering.

My appreciation for you all is immeasurable.

I am ALL that I am,

in great part,

because of you.

I AM a good friend BECAUSE I CHOOSE to be kind.
I always keep my friends' feelings in mind.
I think of how I'd feel if I were in their shoes.
That's called empathy and empathy is pretty cool.

I AM a very good student BECAUSE I CHOOSE to read.

Leaders are readers, and I CHOOSE to lead.

The more that I know the easier it'll be to succeed.

And I CHOOSE success, so I CHOOSE to read.

I AM excellent at sports BECAUSE I CHOOSE to practice.

If I don't get it right the first time,
I just get right back at it!

My mom calls that perseverance,
but I just call it fun.

I love playing sports! Am I the only one?

6

I AM responsible BECAUSE

I CHOOSE to complete my tasks.

Whether I'm at home or at school,

I finish them without being asked.

And that usually works out pretty well for me.

No problem with parents or teachers;

I call that smooth sailing.

I AM healthy BECAUSE

I CHOOSE to eat good food.

Somehow fruits and vegetables

always brighten my mood!

They give me good energy

and vitamins too!

Without healthy snacks,

I don't know what I would do!

I AM strong BECAUSE I CHOOSE to exercise and play!

To be honest, I wish that I could play most of the day.

I run, I jump, I laugh and I scream!

Is there anyone else out there who knows what I mean?

I AM respectful BECAUSE I CHOOSE to listen quietly,

especially when adults are speaking to me.

I respect my elders and my elders respect me.

And when we work together,

we make a pretty good team!

You see, to choose

means to pick something,

and that's a thing that we all do.

Like deciding if you'd rather go to

the park, or instead, go to the zoo.

WILL REMEMBER TO DO MY HOMEWORK
WILL REMEMBER TO DO MY HOMEWORK
WILL REMEMBER TO DO MY HOMEWORK
WILL REMEMBER TO DO MY HOMEWORK
WILL REMEMBER TO DO MY HOMEWORK
WILL REMEMBER TO DO M

A consequence is what
happens after every
choice that you make.
And it can be good or bad,
even if your choice was a mistake.

So to be the best person that I can,

making good choices is the key!

Considering the consequences of my

choices helps me to CHOOSE wisely.

My choices are my SUPERPOWER,

because the only person who can make them is me!

That's why I CHOOSE to be excellent!

What do you CHOOSE to be?

Glossary Terms

Choose
to pick one or more from a group

Consequence
something that happens as a result of something else

Perseverance
to continue to try to do something even though it is difficult

Empathy
The ability to share and understand someone else's feelings

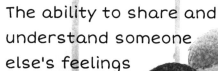

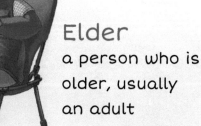

Elder
a person who is older, usually an adult

Respectful

showing or having respect.

Respect is understanding that something or someone is important or serious and should be treated in an appropriate way.

Responsible

able to be trusted to do what is right, expected or required

Success

when something goes well or you reach your goal

Task

a duty or activity that needs to be completed

About the Author

Patrice McLaurin is an author, image activist and character education consultant. She enjoys a good game of Scrabble and loves to read an exciting thriller! She considers herself a teacher, (by calling, not by trade), and an advocate for children. She has worked to empower and enhance the lives of young people for the past two decades.

Her first children's book, "Have You Thanked an Inventor Today?" is an Amazon Best Seller and was acclaimed by Microsoft as a book that informs and inspires STEM. The book received a 5 Star Award from Reader's Favorite and has been greatly received by educators, parents and students alike. Her follow up book, "Have You Thanked a KidVentor Today?" is another great STEM read that highlights some of the wonderful contributions of child inventors. The goal of both books is to encourage children to recognize and tap into their own genius.

Her latest book, I Am Because I Choose is an engaging picture book that encourages children to embrace their most amazing SUPERPOWER which is their power to CHOOSE! Each page demonstrates how children can become whatever it is that they choose to be while highlighting the positive consequences that can result from making good choices.

Patrice McLaurin is a native of Bessemer, AL and a proud graduate of Alabama A&M University. She currently resides in Dacula, GA with her husband and two children.

patricemclaurin.com
facebook.com/thankaninventor
instagram.com/patricemclaurin
twitter.com/mclaurinwrites
pmclaurin@patricemclaurin.com

Other Titles Available

Have You Thanked an Inventor Today? is a unique journey into the often forgotten contributions of the African-American inventors that have greatly enriched America's landscape. It chronicles the school day of a little boy, highlighting different inventions that he uses throughout his day, all of which were invented by Black people. The book comes complete with brief biographies about each inventor, as well as activities that encourage and promote reading comprehension and retention.

*Have You Thanked an Inventor Today is an Amazon Best Seller, a Microsoft Acclaimed STEM Book and it received the 5 Star Award from Reader's Favorite.

Have You Thanked a KidVentor Today? highlights some of our least talked about inventors which are children! In this book, children learn the stories behind some of their favorite inventions, to include the Popsicle and the trampoline! Additionally, to increase vocabulary and promote innovation, Have You Thanked a Kidventor Today comes complete with a glossary and fun science experiments! These wonderful additions are sure to spark any child's natural curiosity!

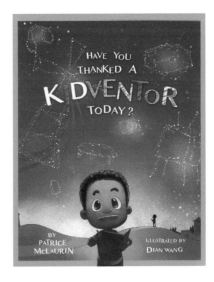

Books are available at patricemclaurin.com, the following online retailers and anywhere that books are sold!

  iBooks

CPSIA information can be obtained
at www.ICGtesting.com
Printed in the USA
BVHW022154200821
614851BV00008B/732